Maximus Mouse's Christmas Card

and other Christmas plays

Scripture Union

© Scripture Union 1999

First published 1999

Scripture Union, 207–209 Queensway, Bletchley, Milton Keynes MK2 2EB, England.

ISBN 1 85999 333 8

Cover illustration: Elke Counsell
Cover design: David Lund

Printed and bound in Great Britain by Ebenezer Baylis & Son Limited, The Trinity Press, Worcester and London.

Maximus Mouse's Christmas Card

by
Brian Ogden

An introduction

During the first part of the play, Maximus Mouse delivers his Christmas cards to his friends. He learns what Christmas means to each of the animals. Maximus' Christmas card then comes to life and he learns what Christmas means to the characters in the nativity story, represented on the Christmas Card.

Maximus delivers Christmas cards to:
Patrick and Paula (both mice)
the Mouselings (their children)
Harold the hedgehog
Barnabas the church bat

Christmas card characters
Mary
Gabriel
Joseph
3 Shepherds
3 Sheep
4 Wise men
3 Innkeepers
Roman Soldier

The Choir have a very important role in the play. Not only do they sing the link verses but they also display a number of visual aids at various times throughout the drama.

The acting area will need a table and chair for the first part.

Carols to be sung by the audience have been included. These are an important aspect of the drama.

Welcome and Introduction

All sing first carol
One of the following would be appropriate:

*Come and join the celebration (See the shepherds hurry down
to Bethlehem)
Tell out my soul, the greatness of the Lord
Angels from the realms of glory*

During the carol **Maximus** *enters, sits at the table, and writes his
Christmas cards. The table is in use throughout the first part of the
play.*

The **children's choir** *are in position throughout the play. They will
need their various visual aids to hand.*

The **choir** *each hold large Christmas cards and do appropriate
actions as the song is sung.*

Choir sing
To the tune of 'This is the way'

Don't forget to write your cards,
Write your cards,
Write your cards,
Don't forget to write your cards
And don't be late for Christmas.

Lots of love and lick it up,
Lick it up,
Lick it up,
Lots of love and lick it up,
And don't be late for Christmas.

Take your cards and hand them out,
Hand them out,
Hand them out,
Take your cards and hand them out,
And don't be late for Christmas.

Maximus *finishes writing his cards and slowly reads out the names
on the envelopes. As he does so, the characters walk behind him
carrying the items listed below.* **Maximus** *ignores them.*

Maximus   There's one for Patrick, my best friend.
(Holding Financial Times)

Maximus   One for Paula, who's very kind.
(Stirring a bowl)

Maximus   One for their mouselings, from their Uncle
Maximus.
(Chattering about their presents)

Maximus   One for Harold the hedgehog, who hibernates in
winter.
*(**Harold** is carried past on a stretcher or wheelbarrow)*

Maximus   One for Barnabas the bat, who wakes up at night.
(Has a bandaged wing)

Maximus   Well, I've written my cards but I wonder what
Christmas really means. Perhaps I shall find out as I deliver
them.

Maximus *puts his cards in a bag and goes off.*

> **Choir sing** *(tune as before)*
> Take your cards and hand them out,
> Hand them out,
> Hand them out,
> Take your cards and hand them out,
> And don't be late for Christmas.

Patrick *enters and sits at the table. He counts some money.*
The choir get ready to hold up their posters.

Maximus *comes in and hands* **Patrick** *his Christmas card.*

Maximus   Hi, Patrick, I've brought your Christmas card.
Is ... 'er ... everything all right? You look worried.

Patrick   Oh, hello, Maximus. Thank you for the card.
Yes, I am worried. That's why I was counting my money. We
always spend too much at Christmas.

Maximus   Yes, I know what you mean. It can be very
expensive.

Patrick   There's *food* to buy to feed us all.
There's *decorations* and a *Christmas tree*.
There's *cards* to send and postage too.
There's *presents* for all the family.

*(**Choir** hold up posters of each item in italics as **Patrick** mentions
them)*

Maximus   So, Patrick, is Christmas about spending lots of
money?

Patrick   Well, it is to me, Maximus. That's why I'm so worried.

Maximus   I'm sure there's more to it than that. I do hope Christmas won't cost you too much. Bye, now.

Patrick *and* **Maximus** *leave in opposite directions.*

Maximus *re-enters as* **Paula** *comes on from the other side. She stands at the table, stirring her bowl.*

> **Choir sing**
> Take your cards and hand them out.

Maximus   Hello, Paula. Busy I see.

Paula   Always twice as busy before Christmas. What do you want, Maximus?

Maximus   Here's your Christmas card.

Paula   Thanks, but I can't stop to look now. I've got forty-three mouselings to feed.

> I've got to get this *pudding* stirred,
> And *presents* wrapped without delay,
> And *cards* sent out to all our friends,
> I'll never finish by Christmas Day.

Choir *mime stirring bowls, wrapping presents and writing cards.*

Maximus   Oh dear, Paula, you are busy.

Paula   I must get this cheese pudding stirred. I'm far too busy for Christmas.

Maximus   I hope it'll all be ready in time. Happy Christmas, Paula.

Paula *goes off still stirring the bowl.* **Maximus** *sits down.*

> **Choir sing**
> Take your cards and hand them out

The **mouselings** *(no limit on the number) come in chattering about the Christmas presents they want. Update the presents where necessary.*

Mouseling I   I want roller blades.

Mouseling 2   I want a Barbie Doll.

Mouseling 3   I want a Mousehampton United kit.

Mouseling 4   I want a new mousecoat.

Mouseling 5   I want a computer game.

Mouseling 6   And I want all of them!

Maximus (*shouts above the noise*) I've got something for you all.

Mouselings *crowd round* **Maximus** *who gives his Christmas card to one of them.*

Mouseling 7   Oh, it's only a Christmas card.

Mouselings (*sounding disappointed*) 'Er ... thank you, Uncle Maximus.

Maximus   So is Christmas about wanting lots of presents?

Mouselings   Oh, yes.

Mouseling 1   Lots

Mouseling 2   and lots

Mouseling 3   and lots

Mouseling 4   and lots

Mouseling 6   and lots

Mouseling 7   of presents.

Mouseling 1   I want roller blades to skate along,

Mouseling 2   I want the Mice Girls' latest song,

Mouseling 3   I want a new computer game,

Mouseling 4   And I want a picture in a frame.

Maximus   Well, I hope you get all the presents you want.

The **mouselings** *run off, still chattering about their presents.*

Choir sing
Take your cards and hand them out

Choir put on night caps.

Harold *the hedgehog walks on slowly. He is wearing a night cap and is wrapped in a blanket and has a hot water bottle hanging down. He is yawning.*

Maximus   Hello, Harold. Have you just woken up?

Harold   No, I couldn't get to sleep. It's all these children practising their Christmas play! And it's freezing outside the church.

Maximus   I've brought you a Christmas card.

Harold   Thanks, Maximus, but I'm not looking forward to Christmas. It's such a cold time of the year. There's no one about in the churchyard – no animals to talk to.

Maximus   You must get very lonely?

Harold   Yes, Christmas is a very lonely time for some of us.

I'm on my own, no friends around,
Too hard to sleep on frozen ground.
Christmas can be very cold –
Especially when you're growing old!

Harold *curls up in a ball and goes to sleep, snoring from time to time.*

Maximus   'er ... goodnight, Harold. Happy Christmas.

Choir sing
Take your cards and hand them out

Maximus *looks at the last card.* **Barnabas**, *the church bat, flies in very slowly. One of his wings is heavily bandaged.*

Maximus   Barnabas, what have you done?

Barnabas   It's Christmas! I forgot the world goes mad at Christmas. Some silly human put a tree in the church and I flew straight into it. People just don't think about us bats.

Maximus   I do hope you aren't too badly hurt. By the way, I've brought your Christmas card.

Barnabas   Thanks, Maximus. I'll try and put it where I won't bump into it.

Christmas time is far from jolly,
Crashing into bits of holly!
Please remember, don't forget –
It can be dangerous for your pet.

Must fly *(bumps into Maximus)* ... or at least try.

Maximus   Barnabas, I do hope you have a safe Christmas.

Barnabas *flies off with difficulty.*
Harold *is taken off on a stretcher or wheelbarrow still fast asleep.*

> **Choir sing**
> We've written our cards and handed them out,
> Handed them out,
> Handed them out,
> We've written our cards and handed them out,
> So they're not late for Christmas.

Maximus   So Christmas means spending money, being very busy, wanting presents, feeling lonely and putting up with decorations. Surely there's more to Christmas than that?

*As **Maximus** speaks, the animals walk behind him carrying the items as at the start of the play. **Maximus** ignores them again.*

Maximus *settles down in his chair and goes to sleep.*

> **All sing a Carol**
> Any one of the following are appropriate :
>
> *O little town of Bethlehem*
> *The first Nowell the angel did say*
> *O come, all ye faithful*

As the carol is sung the nativity figures come on. As the carol ends Maximus wakes up. He rubs his eyes and looks amazed at what he sees in front of him.

Maximus   But ... that's my Christmas card picture! It's, 'er, ... come to life! Perhaps now I really can find out what Christmas means.

Mary steps forward

Mary   Christmas for me started with an angel. Gabriel came from God with a message.

Gabriel steps forward

Gabriel   Mary, God has chosen you. You will become the mother of God's son, Jesus.

Mary   I could hardly believe it. God had chosen me! Me of all people.

Gabriel   His name will be Jesus.
He will be called the Son of the Most High.
The Lord God will make him a king.

Gabriel *returns to group*

Mary   The angel was right. Soon I could feel the baby growing inside me and I was really looking forward to my son being born at home. But the Romans had other ideas.

Roman soldier *steps forward with manuscript*

Roman Soldier
Augustus has spoken,
And you must obey,
To your own town or city –
You must do what I say.
There you must register,
The Emperor decrees.
Taxes are vital,
You must pay our fees.

Roman soldier *returns to group*

Mary   So Christmas for me meant a long journey and the birth of Jesus, the son of God.

Choir sing
(Tune: Skye Boat song)

Gabriel came, a message to bring,
'You are God's chosen one,
To carry the babe, born to be King,
Jesus, his only son.

Mary *returns to the group.* **Joseph** *steps forward.*

Joseph   It was a shock. My wife Mary being chosen by God. But first we had to make the journey to Bethlehem. It was a long way and we went slowly for Mary's sake. By the time we got to Bethlehem all the rooms were taken.

Three Innkeepers *wearing aprons step forward.*

Innkeeper 1   Sorry mate, not a room in the house.

Innkeeper 2   Can't help you, we're full right up.

Innkeeper 3   Best I can do is the stable. You're welcome to that.

> **Innkeepers sing** – *(with support of the **choir** if necessary)*
> *Tune: Three Blind Mice*
>
> Full right up,
> Full right up,
> All beds are let,
> All beds are let.
> There's not a room left in the house,
> We couldn't accommodate a mouse,
> Not even Joseph and his spouse,
> We're full right up.

Maximus   I know that tune! Play it again, Sam.

Innkeepers sing *Full right up* song again

Innkeepers *return to group.*

Joseph   It was the stable or the street. We were grateful to have that. I made Mary as comfortable as possible and very soon Jesus was born. Mary nursed him in her arms and then I put Jesus into the manger so Mary could sleep.

> **Choir sing**
> *Tune: Skye Boat song*
>
> Bethlehem town, and nowhere to stay,
> Joseph a worried man.
> Into the stable, without delay,
> All part of God's great plan.

Joseph   So Christmas for me meant a helpless baby and a stable for the birth of the Son of God.

> **All sing**
> *Away in a manger*

*During the carol **Joseph** returns to the group and four **shepherds** step forward each with their own **sheep**.*

Shepherd 1   It was a dark night on the hilltop.

Shepherd 2   A wolf was howling close by.

Shepherd 3   How do you know? You were asleep!

Shepherd 4   Well, I wasn't. You lot made me stay awake.

Shepherd 1   It was your turn.

Shepherd 4   It was my turn last night and the night before that.

Shepherd 2   Angels. Thousands of angels.

Shepherd 3   All singing beautifully.

Shepherd 4   Then one of them spoke.

Gabriel *steps forward*

Gabriel   Don't be afraid.

Shepherd 4   I wasn't.

Shepherd 3   Not much you weren't.

Gabriel   I have good news for you. Down in Bethlehem a baby has been born. He is the Saviour – Christ the Lord. You'll find him lying in a manger.

Gabriel *returns to group.*

Shepherds and sheep sing
Tune: The Grand Old Duke of York

Oh, the shepherds of Bethlehem,
They had ten thousand sheep,
They marched them up to the top of the hill,
And then they went to sleep.

Sheep *lie down on the floor asleep*
Shepherds *move up and down according to the words of the chorus.*

And when they were up, they were up,
And when they were down, they were down,
And when they were only half way up,
They were neither up nor down

Shepherds *and* **sheep** *perform a dance to the chorus between each verse*

12

Oh, the angels of the Lord,
Sang praises to his name,
And told the shepherds they must run,
To the stable in Bethlehem.

And when they were up, they were up,
And when they were down, they were down,
And when they were only half way up,
They were neither up, nor down.

Oh, the shepherds ran so fast,
And found the babe asleep,
They knelt down there, and worshipped him,
Then went back to their sheep.

And when they were up, they were up,
And when they were down, they were down,
And when they were only half way up,
They were neither up nor down.

Shepherd 1   Amazing.

Shepherd 2   Excellent

Shepherd 3   Fantastic

Shepherd 4   Fabulous

Shepherds Together   Christmas means that God has come
into the world as a baby.

Shepherds and **sheep** *return to the group during the song*

Choir sing
Tune: Skye Boat song

Loud angels cry, mighty their praise,
'Jesus is born,' they sing,
Shepherds look stunned, sky is ablaze,
'Jesus is born, our King.'

Four Wise men *step forward, three of them carrying gifts.*

Wise man 1 *looks at the other Wise men and counts them*

Wise man 1   One, two, three, ... four! Excuse me, but haven't
we got one too many?

Wise man 2   Well, it isn't me.

Wise man 3 It isn't me either.

Wise man 4 And it certainly isn't me.

Wise man 1 Oh dear, it must be me.

Wise man 2 Not if you read your Bible.

Wise man 3 It doesn't say how many of us there were.

Wise man 1 That's all right then, I'll stay.

Wise man 4 That's good – it's your map!

> **All sing a carol**
> Any one of the following are appropriate
>
> *As with gladness men of old*
> *The first Nowell the angel did say*

During the carol **Mary** *and* **Joseph** *step forward and stand with the* **Wise men**.
The **Wise men** *in turn present their gifts which are taken by* **Joseph**.

Wise man 1 I bring gold, the king of metals, for Jesus, the King.

Wise man 2 I bring frankincense, a sweet-smelling perfume, to worship Jesus, the Lord.

Wise man 3 I bring myrrh, a sign of death, for Jesus who will die as our Saviour.

Wise man 4 I have no gift but myself to bring to Jesus. He is the King, the Lord and the Saviour. As God gave Jesus to us at Christmas so wise men give themselves in return.

All Wise men   And that is the meaning of Christmas.

Wise men return to group during song

> **Choir sing**
> *Tune: Skye Boat song*
>
> Wise men brought gifts as their offering,
> Frankincense, gold and myrrh,
> Wise men today still worship the King,
> Jesus, our great Saviour.

Maximus steps forward to the centre of the acting area

Maximus So my card shows the real meaning of Christmas

A prayer read by Maximus

Lord Jesus,
help us to learn that the true meaning of Christmas is not how much we spend, how busy we are or how many presents we get. It is that your Son Jesus was born in a stable, lived as a man and died as our Saviour.
Amen

All sing final carol
One of the following would be appropriate

O little town of Bethlehem
Silent night
Once in Royal David's city
See him lying on a bed of straw

Isn't he Beautiful?

by
Daphne Kitching

Characters

Mother
Child
Jane
Sarah
Sam
Joseph
Mary
Angel 1
Angel 2
Shepherd 1
Shepherd 2
Shepherd 3
Wise man 1
Wise man 2
Wise man 3
Reader
Extra shoppers

Spaces have been left for the suggested names of the new child by the friends. It is suggested that names of current favourite pop stars or sports heroes be used to add interest.

Everyone sings:
"Isn't he beautiful?" or, if this is unfamiliar, *"Jesus, name above all names"*

(The tunes for these songs can be found in Songs and Hymns of Fellowship *and many other books of modern Christian songs)*

Reader   Isaiah, Chapter 9, verse 6.
A child is born to us!
A son is given to us!
And he will be our ruler.
He will be called Wonderful Counsellor,
Mighty God,
Eternal Father,
Prince of Peace.

Our play starts in a busy street on Christmas Eve. Shoppers bustle about greeting each other... A mother comes along with her new baby in his pram and her other child. She meets some friends.

Mother   Hello, Jane and Sarah. Come and see my new baby boy – it's our first trip out!

Jane   Oh let me see him. Isn't he beautiful, what's he called? *(looking into the pram)*

Mother   We haven't decided yet. Have you any ideas?

Jane   Oh, yes. I'd call him _____ or _____!

Sarah *(Looking into the pram and shaking her head)* No, he looks more like a _____ or an _____ to me. What do you think, Sam?

(Pulls her husband into the group)

Sam   He looks like his grandad to me. Call him Frederick after his grandad. Or Noel, seeing as it's Christmas. Frederick Noel, how about that?

Mother   Oh, I don't know. They're all nice names, it's hard to choose. Perhaps we could use all of them! _____, _____, _____, _____, Frederick, Noel Smith!

(Insert suggested modern names in the spaces eg. Michael, Owen , Ronaldo etc)

Child   Come on, Mum, I'm cold. Why do we have to do all this Christmas shopping? What's so special about Christmas?

Mother   Well, this Christmas is special for us because we have our new baby boy, and the very first Christmas was special for the very same reason. A new baby boy was born. I wonder if Mary and Joseph had the same problems in choosing a name!

Child (*Pulling the mother off stage*) That's no problem, we'll just call him Fred. Fred... Fred... Fred!

Scene 2 Bethlehem

(*The stable with* **Mary**, **Joseph** *and the baby. An* **angel** *stands beside a wall board or free standing display unit on which he pins the names of Jesus as they are mentioned. They are in italics in the text below*)

Mary (*Looking at Jesus*) Oh, Joseph, isn't he beautiful?

Joseph   Yes Mary, he's wonderful. What did you say the angel told you to call him?

Mary   He said we should call him *Jesus*. But he also said he would be called the *Son of God*.

Joseph   It's a bit puzzling, you know, because the angel in my dream told me Jesus, but he also said he would be called *Immanuel*, which means "God with us". Jesus, Son of God, Immanuel. Quite a mouthful!

Mary   Look Joseph, here come some visitors!

(*Enter the* **shepherds**, *directed by an angel*)

Shepherd 1   May we come in to see your baby?

Mary   Yes, you are very welcome. Here he is.

Shepherd 2   Isn't he beautiful, really beautiful?

Shepherd 3   It's true then, what those angels said. They said we would find the child lying in a manger and here he is! They also said that this baby will be called our *Saviour*.

Shepherd 1   And they told us he would be the *Prince of Peace*.

(Angel puts up the new names)

Joseph   Two more names for the baby! Saviour and Prince of Peace. How will I remember them all?

(Enter the Wise men)

Wise man 1   We have brought gifts for this special baby king. Mine is gold.

Wise man 2   My gift is frankincense. Where is the child who will be known as *Almighty God* to all the world?

Joseph   Another name to add to the list!

*(**Angel** adds it)*

Wise man 3   I bring myrrh for this baby boy who will show the world how to be friends with God if only people will put their trust in him. Isn't he beautiful?

Mary   What a lot of visitors! And what a lot of names my baby seems to have!

(She reads them from the Angel's list)

Jesus, Son of God, Immanuel, Saviour, Prince of Peace, Almighty God. We can't use all those every time we call to him! I think we'll just call him Jesus – I like that name above all the other names. Yes, we'll just call him Jesus.

Everyone joins in to sing, *"Jesus, name above all names".*

The Christmas Tree

by
Marjory Francis

Characters

Speaking parts:
Three children, A, B and C
Narrator (This part can be read)
Mary
Joseph
Innkeeper
Three shepherds
Angel
Three wise men
Decoration 1
Present 1
Candle 1
(These three should be among those who remain on stage after the songs.)

Non speaking parts:
Snowflakes (any number)
Decorations (at least four)
Presents (at least three)
Candles (at least two)
Star

Stage directions

Arrange the stage area as follows:
At the back and to right of centre stands a very large Christmas tree shape. Make this by asking every child in the production to draw round their hands, cut out the shapes and paint them dark green. Fix them in overlapping lines starting at the bottom, onto a triangle background, with a base about two metres wide.

In front of the tree arrange space for four children to sit on the floor, three on chairs behind them, two standing behind the chairs and one to stand on a stool or box in the centre at the rear.

The main acting and singing will be presented on the centre of the stage. The nativity tableau should be set up at far stage right. You will need a small bench or two stools and a manger. At far stage left position three chairs.

The different groups of children should be seated on the floor area in front of the stage. As they perform their individual pieces they should mount the stage, but for songs sung all together they should remain on the floor area and turn to face the audience. There will be five groups of children: snowflakes, decorations, candles, presents and the actors and nativity tableau.

All stand to sing
Christmas Tree Song
*Tune: O Christmas tree (O Tannenbaum trad, Carol Gaily
Carol) A & C Black*

O Christmas tree with all your lights
Shine brightly on this night of nights.
Your branches ever green will stay
In summer, winter, night and day,
And decorated lovely tree
Your beauty everyone can see.
O Christmas tree with all your lights
Shine brightly on this night of nights.

O Christmas tree stand straight and tall
And shine out to remind us all
Of Christmas time once long ago
In Bethlehem with starlight's glow.
For Jesus, Mary's son was born
And now on every Christmas morn
O Christmas tree stand straight and tall
And shine out to remind us all.

Snowflakes *enter (this can incorporate a dance if you wish).*

Snowflakes sing
Snowflakes' song
*Tune: Coral, amber, pearl and shell (Merrily to Bethlehem),
A & C Black*

Snowflakes falling from the clouds,
Falling gently to the ground,
Cover all with softest white,
Touch the earth without a sound.

Snowflakes fall, softly fall,
Whispering that winter's near.
Snowflakes fall, softly fall,
Whispering that winter's here.

Gently floating from the sky
Covering house and tree and wall
With a feathery blanket white,
See the snowflakes softly fall.

Snowflakes fall etc.

Snowflakes *stand in a semicircle around the rear of the stage or sit
along the front.*

21

Enter **A**, **B** *and* **C**

A   Brrr, isn't it cold today?

B   Yes, it's been snowing hard.

C   It must be nearly Christmas.

A   Let's hurry home. It will be nice and warm there.

B   Let's decorate the Christmas tree when we get home.

C   Good idea.

A, **B** *and* **C** *exit.*

> **Snowflakes sing**
> **Snowflakes' song**

Snowflakes *exit, incorporating a dance if you wish.*

Enter **A**, **B** *(carrying a box) and* **C**.

A   *(indicating tree)* What a lovely big tree!

B   Here's the box of decorations.

C   *(looking into box)* Oh, aren't they pretty!

A   Look, there are bells, and silver balls.

A   And shiny beads and tinsel.

A   They're lovely.

Enter **Decorations**

> **Decorations sing**
> **Decorations' song**
> *Tune: My ship sailed from China (Apusskidu), A & C Black*
>
> The baubles all sparkle in red, gold and green,
> The tinsel shines silver with branches between,
> The glass balls all shine as they hang on the tree,
> A prettier tree you won't see.
>
> Golden bells, diamonds, a bright glistening show,
> Stars and hearts mingle in soft lanterns' glow,
> The glass balls all shine as they hang on the tree
> A prettier tree you won't see.

Four **Decorations** *remain and sit on the floor in front of the tree.*
The rest exit.

A   The decorations look so pretty.

B   Yes, but we haven't finished yet. We must put our
presents on the tree.

C   Have you wrapped yours up?

A   Yes, in lovely paper.

B   Oh, they look exciting!

C   No peeping till Christmas day.

Enter **Presents**

> **Presents sing**
> **Presents' song**
> *Tune: Morningtown ride (Apusskidu), A & C Black*
>
> Presents for Mummy,
> What can be inside?
> Soap or scent or hankies
> In the parcel hide.
>
> *Tied up tight in tinsel,*
> *Wrapped in paper bright,*
> *Hanging on the Christmas tree*
> *Wait for Christmas night.*
>
> Parcels for Daddy,
> Secrets wrapped up well.
> Ties or socks or chocolates?
> We will never tell.
>
> *Tied up tight etc.*
>
> Aunties, uncles, cousins,
> Grandads, grannies too,
> Everyone has presents,
> That means me and you.
>
> *Tied up tight etc.*

Three **Presents** *remain and sit on the chairs behind the*
Decorations. *The rest exit.*

23

A   Our tree must be nearly finished.

B   No, not yet. We haven't got the lights.

C   Let's have candles.

A   Oh yes, candles will be lovely.

B   All different colours.

C   And shining out for Christmas.

Enter **Candles**

Candles sing
Candles' song
Tune: This old man (Trad)

Candles bright in the night
Shining out the Christmas light,
Making darkness seem like day,
Chasing shadows far away.

Candles tall, candles small,
Lovely colours one and all,
Making darkness etc.

Candles shine, yours and mine,
Now our Christmas tree looks fine,
Making darkness etc.

Two **Candles** *remain and stand behind the three* **Presents**. *The rest exit.*

A   There, the tree must be finished now.

B   No, there's one more thing.

C   I know, a star!

A   Oh yes, the star at the top.

B   I wonder why we have a star...

C   And decorations, and presents and candles. Why do we have any of them?

A, **B** *and* **C** *sit on the chairs at far stage left.*

Enter **Narrator**, *standing at stage left.*

Narrator   Long, long ago Mary and Joseph travelled to Bethlehem. They needed somewhere to stay the night.

Enter **Mary** *and* **Joseph** *stage left. Enter* **Innkeeper**, *to stand at stage right.*

Mary   I'm so tired Joseph. Please see if we can stay in the inn.

Innkeeper   No, I am sorry. All the beds are full up. But you can stay in the stable. *(Indicates manger area.)*

Joseph   That is better than nothing. Come along, Mary.

(Mary and Joseph sit on the seats by the manger, Innkeeper stands nearby.)

Narrator   That night Mary's son Jesus was born in the stable. Mary had no bed for the baby, so she put him in the manger.

Decoration I *(Stands.)* We decorate our houses to show that we are happy that it is Jesus' birthday. *(Sits.)*

Enter **Shepherds** *stage left, to stand in the centre.*

Narrator   During the night some shepherds were out on the hillside.

Shepherd I   It is cold tonight.

Enter **Angel**, *stage right.*

Shepherd 2   What is that bright light?

Shepherd 3   I'm frightened!

Angel   Don't be afraid. I have come with good news.

Narrator   The good news was that God had sent his son Jesus. The angel told the shepherds to go to Bethlehem to see him.

The Shepherds go to the manger area, kneel and look at the baby, then stand behind Mary and Joseph.

Present I   (*Stands.*) We give people presents at Christmas because God gave us the best present of all, his Son Jesus. (*Sits.*)

Enter **Wise men** *stage left,* **Star** *stage right.*

Narrator   Some time later in a far off land, some wise men noticed a new star in the sky.

Wise man I   (*Pointing*) Look, there's a new star shining.

Wise man 2   So there is. It must be the star of an important king.

Wise man 3   He must be very special to have his own star. Let's go and visit him.

Candle I   (*Stands.*) We have candles at Christmas to remind us that Jesus is a light for people all over the world. (*Sits.*)

Narrator   The wise men followed the star. It took them all the way to Bethlehem. They gave the baby presents.

The **Star** *moves across the stage towards the manger area, the* **Wise men** *following. The* **Star** *stops behind the manger. The* **Wise men** *kneel before the baby and put their gifts by the manger. They then position themselves around the manger. The* **Star** *goes to stand on the stool in front of the tree.*

All stand except the children in front of the tree and the nativity tableau.

>   **All: sing**
>   **Manger song** (*or Away in a manger*)
>   *Tune: Christmas song (New Child Songs, Denholm House Press, but out of print)*
>
>   Sing for the Baby at Bethlehem,
>   Sing of the shepherds who worshipped him,
>   Sing of the gladness he gave to them
>   And the star that shone.
>
>   Sing of the people who saw the Babe
>   There in the stable at Bethlehem.
>   Sing of the flickering candle flames
>   And the star that shone.
>
>   Sing of the wonderful gifts we see
>   On the glittering boughs of our Christmas tree.
>   The Baby belongs to you and me
>   And his star shines on.

All sit except **A**, **B** *and* **C**, *who come centre stage.*

A   Well, our tree is finished at last.

B   And doesn't it look beautiful!

C   Yes. Happy Christmas everyone!

All stand, with exceptions as before.

All sing Christmas tree song.

Costume notes:
Snowflakes:
White T-shirt or jumper; white pants and tights; soft shoes; length of silver tinsel to go round head.
  Make snowflake costumes from a 50cm (approx) square of white net curtaining (size depends on child). Cut a slit in the centre for the child's head to go through, and large zigzags round the edge. Put elastic loops on two diagonal corners for the child's fingers. Wear the costume with points hanging down the front and back.

Decorations:
Any brightly coloured clothes. On the front fasten with a safety pin a large shape (circle, diamond, bell, heart or lantern) made from card. The shape is decorated as brightly as possible with tinsel, shiny paper, glitter etc. A decorative headdress could be worn if wished.

Presents:
Any brightly coloured clothes. On the front fasten with a safety pin a large rectangle or square card, covered with Christmas wrapping paper. Stick strips of paper or ribbon across with a bow in the centre. Add a large label if you wish.

Candles:
Basic clothes in a plain colour. On the front fasten with a safety pin a large rectangle of red card, with a small white card centre top for the 'wick'. Make flame headdresses from a band of cards with a flame shape fastened to it, if possible making the flame extend down the sides of the face. Decorate the flame with red, orange and gold shiny paper.

Children A, B and C:
Bright play clothes; scarves, hats and gloves for the first scene.

Narrator:
Long robe or 'smart' clothes; large book or folder decorated with Christmas paper or labelled 'The Christmas Story'.

Bible Characters:
Traditional

Star:
White or silver robe; headband with a large star on the front, or a garden cane with a large star on it to hold up.

The Little Star

by
Marjory Francis

Characters

Speaking parts:
Little Star
Narrator
Orion's Belt (three children)
Moon
Sun
Jupiter
Venus
Pole Star
Mercury
Saturn
Mars
Trees (five)
Birds (four)
Teacher
Children (up to seven)
Readers (up to three)
Children dressed as Mary and Joseph, innkeeper (optional), angels,
shepherds and wise men

Non speaking parts:
Various stars (the Milky Way)
Trees
Birds
Shoppers

You will need a stage area big enough to accommodate each group as they come on to sing their song, plus an acting area. For much of the time the Little Star is an observer, so will stand at the side of the stage, while the main action happens in the centre. The nativity tableau should be set up in the centre of the stage. Use plain curtains, or dark blue with small silver stars as a background

Stage directions
Each group of children (Planets etc, Milky Way, trees, birds, shoppers, teacher and class) should sit in a block in front and to the side of the stage facing. They should mount the stage and position themselves for their performance and resume their seats on the floor afterwards. For some renderings of the Star Song and the Finale Song everyone should stand and face the audience to sing.

The narrator should be in a prominent position at the side of the stage.

Narrator   Once upon a time there was a little star who lived high up in the sky.

Enter **Little Star** *leaping around.*

Narrator   She liked to watch everything that was happening down on the earth.

Little Star *goes to a position at the side.*

> **Everyone stands to sing**
> **The star song**
> *Tune: Twinkle, twinkle (trad)*
>
> Twinkle, twinkle, little star,
> How I wonder what you are.
> Up above the world so high,
> Like a diamond in the sky.
> Twinkle, twinkle, little star,
> How I wonder what you are.
>
> Twinkle, twinkle, little star,
> Do you see us from afar?
> Do you watch us passing by
> As you shine up in the sky?
> Twinkle, twinkle, little star,
> Do you see us from afar?

All sit except **Narrator** *and* **Little Star**.

Narrator   Every now and again there was a gathering of all the stars and planets so that they could talk about what they had seen and heard.

Enter some of the **Milky Way** *who cross the stage in groups and exit.*

Narrator   The little star set off to join them, but she was very slow because she was so busy watching the earth.

Enter **Orion's Belt**.

Orion 1   Are you coming to the gathering?

Orion 2   You'd better hurry up.

Orion 3   You'll be late.

Orion 1   Of course, she's only a little star.

Orion 2   Not three in a row like us – Orion's Belt.

Orion 3   Yes, we're important!

Exit **Orion's Belt***, walking slowly and chatting.*

Little Star   I ought to be going, but this earth place is so interesting, and I've such a good view here.

Enter **Sun** *and* **Moon***.*

Moon   It's awfully kind of you, Sun, to lend me your light.

Sun   Well, I like to be warm-hearted. And after all, we are neighbours, even if I am ninety-three million miles away. You look slimmer, Moon. Have you been on a diet?

Moon   I'm trying to keep off the cream cheese. But I always seem to get fat again, somehow.

Exit **Sun** *and* **Moon** *walking slowly and chatting.*

Little Star   There go Sun and Moon. I'd better be going.

Enter **Pole Star** *walking quickly.*

Little Star   Ah, here comes the Pole Star. If I follow him I won't get lost.

Pole Star *crosses stage and exits.* **Little Star** *follows.*

> **Remaining seated, all sing:**
> **Star song** (repeat)

Enter **Jupiter***,* **Venus***,* **Pole Star***,* **Milky Way** *and* **Little Star***.*

Jupiter   Is everybody here yet, Venus?

Venus   There are one or two more to come, Jupiter. I haven't seen Mars yet.

Pole Star   The Milky Way are all here I see. Let's ask them to sing for us.

*The **Milky Way** group position themselves and sing:*

Milky Way song
Tune: Donkey Riding (trad)

Stars are shining way up high, making patterns in the sky,
You can't count us though you try – we're the Milky Way.

High, high, way up high,
Shining brightly, shining brightly,
High, high, way up high,
We're the Milky Way.

Sparkling millions, twinkling bright, shining on the darkest
night,
Sending out our brilliant light – we're the Milky Way.

High, high…

Jupiter   That was lovely.

*Enter **Mercury**.*

Jupiter   Ah, Mercury, have you any messages for us?

Mercury   Only that Mars is on his way. Something made
him see red and he's picked a quarrel with Saturn.

Venus   Oh, Saturn will run rings around him. But let's
hope they make up their quarrel quickly. We want to enjoy
ourselves at our heavenly gathering.

*Enter **Sun**, **Moon** and **Orion's Belt**.*

Venus   And here are a few more people. Welcome Sun
and Moon. Welcome Orion's Belt.

Narrator   The little star felt that nobody was really
interested in her. She was too little and unimportant, so she
just sat in a corner to listen.

Mercury   Isn't it good to see everyone?

Sun   And what wonderful sights we've all seen
down on the earth.

Moon   They are building amazingly tall buildings now,
you know.

Venus   I can remember seeing the leaning tower of Pisa built – but it was straight then.

Pole Star   My memory must be better than yours, because I can remember them working on the Pyramids in Egypt.

Little Star   I don't remember any of this. I'm too little.

Enter **Saturn** *and* **Mars**.

Mercury   Oh, hello, Mars and Saturn. Have you made up your quarrel?

Mars   Yes, thank you. Chocolate can work wonders. You should try sharing a Mars bar a day.

Sun   We were talking of all the wonderful things we've seen. We have such a good view from up here.

Saturn   Do you remember that strange new star? He only came one year. He said he saw some really amazing sights.

Orion 1   Yes, wasn't it odd? A baby born in a stable, and shepherds coming…

Orion 2   And angels singing. Don't forget the angels!

Orion 3   Yes, and there were some rich men who came to visit. The star said he led the way.

Pole Star   And we've never seen him again. It's a real mystery. He called himself the Star of Bethlehem and said it was the first Christmas.

Narrator   The Little Star felt she had never heard such a lovely story. Angels! Rich men! And a baby! How she would love to see them too! Then she had an idea. She would go down to earth. She would try to see what the Star of Bethlehem saw. So she set off straight away.

Exit **Little Star**. *Exit other stars and planets.*

> **All Stand to sing:**
> **Star song**

Enter **Trees**. *They stand in position, with the speakers at the front.*

Narrator   The Little Star landed on the earth a place where there were lots of trees.

Enter **Little Star**.

Little Star   Where am I?

Tree 1   This is the forest.

Tree 2   We are all the fir trees.

Tree 3   We look ordinary now but soon we will be Christmas trees.

Little Star   Christmas trees! I've come to earth to find out something to do with Christmas. Can you tell me all about it?

Tree 4   We'll sing you our song.

> **Trees sing:**
> **Tree song**
> *Tune: Clementine (trad)*
>
> Little seeds are blown by breezes,
> Landing gently on the earth,
> Start to grow in rain and sunshine,
> Tiny trees have come to birth.
>
> Brave new branches stretching upwards
> Grow towards the bright blue sky.
> Prickly needles, green and spiky,
> Point to clouds as they pass by.
>
> Now we've all grown tall and stately,
> None can be as fine as these.
> We are green and straight and splendid.
> Soon we'll all be Christmas trees.

Little Star   Thank you, but I still haven't found out much about Christmas.

Tree 5   You will have to go into town. That's where we go to become Christmas trees.

Exit **Trees**.

Little Star   Oh dear, who will help me find my way to town?

Enter **Birds 1** *and* **2**.

Bird 1　　　　We can help you.

Bird 2　　　　We're the birds.

Enter **Bird 3** *and* **Bird chorus**.

Bird 3　　　　We always go to the town in the winter. People put out lots of food for us.

Little Star　　Oh thank you.

> **Birds sing:**
> **Birds' song**
> *Tune: Morningtown ride*
>
> Birds in the springtime build their nests and sing,
> Lay their eggs and hatch them all because it's Spring.
>
> *Singing to us sweetly all around the year,*
> *Don't forget the hungry birds now that Winter's here.*
>
> Birds in the Summer sing up in the trees,
> Visiting our gardens with butterflies and bees.
>
> *Singing to us sweetly …*
>
> Birds in the Autumn look for berries bright,
> Singing in the hedgerows from the dawn till night.
>
> *Singing to us sweetly …*

Bird 1　　　　Here we are at the town. You should be all right now.

Bird 2　　　　We're off to find some delicious crumbs!

Exit **Birds**.

Narrator　　The Little Star thanked the birds and looked around at the town. Perhaps here she would see what the Star of Bethlehem saw. When some people came along she decided to hide and watch.

Little Star *moves to far edge of stage.*

Enter **Shoppers** *from different directions. They move busily across the stage freezing between verses as they sing:*

The Shoppers' song
Tune: This old man (trad)

Shopping here, shopping there,
Buying all our Christmas fare.
Come and spend your money, come and spend it here,
Christmas day is very near.

Buying here, buying there,
Things to give and food to share.
Come and spend …

Rushing here, rushing there,
Busy shoppers everywhere.
Come and spend …

Exit **Shoppers.**

Little Star   Those people were talking about Christmas, but was that really what the Star of Bethlehem saw? Lots of people rushing around, too busy to stop? I don't think so.

Narrator   The Little Star was very sad. Perhaps she would never find out about Christmas. Then she saw some children with their teacher.

Enter **Teacher** *shepherding* **Children** *in pairs. They sit in a group on the stage.*

Narrator   She decided to follow them into school.

Little Star *follows* **Children** *and 'hides' in another corner.*

Teacher   Now, children, today we are going to act the Christmas story.

Child 1   I'll get the manger.

Puts manger in centre. **Children** *in Bible costumes move to positions as they are mentioned (see below).* **Readers** *stand in a line towards the back and* **Children** *numbered one to seven sit in a group around the* **Teacher.**

Child 2   The shepherds can wait over here.

Teacher   Angels, you wait here as well.

Child 3   The wise men will be over this side.

35

Teacher　　Mary and Joseph, are you ready?

Reader 1　　One night Mary and Joseph arrived in Bethlehem.

Mary *and* **Joseph** *move to centre.*

Reader 1　　They had nowhere to stay and the inn was full, so they had to stay in the stable.

Little Star　　I do believe I've found Christmas at last!

Reader 1　　Mary's baby was born in the stable. She called him Jesus and laid him in the manger.

Reader 2　　Angels sang to shepherds in the fields.

All those on stage sing:
Angels' song
Tune: Lullaby, Jesus, my dear one (Carol Gaily 9)

On the dark hillside the angels are singing,
Good news from heaven the angels are bringing.

Sing to the shepherds and praise with our voices.
At the glad message all heaven rejoices.

In the dark stable a baby is sleeping.
'Peace to all people' – his promise is keeping.

Sing to the shepherds...

Reader 2　　The shepherds hurried to the stable to see the baby Jesus.

Little Star　　This is it! This is the story the Star of Bethlehem saw!

Reader 3　　There were some wise men in the east who studied the stars. One day a new star appeared.

Child 4　　Oh, we have forgotten the star.

Child 5　　Who shall we choose?

Little Star　　Please,

Little Star *steps forward.*

Little Star   Can I help you?

Child 6   Who are you?

Child 7   You look just like a real star!

Little Star   I would like to be the star in your story.

Teacher   Of course you can. Carry on, storyteller.

Reader 3   The wise men followed the star. It led them to Bethlehem.

Little Star *leads way to manger.*

Reader 3   The wise men gave their gifts to the baby Jesus.

> **Everyone sings** (*the groups on floor remaining seated*):
> **Manger song** (*or* **Away in a manger**)
> *Tune: He smiles within his cradle (Merrily to Bethlehem 11),*
> *A & C Black*
>
> The baby in the stable
> Born on this winter's night,
> Who lies within the manger,
> Is Christ the Lord of light,
> And came from heaven's height.
>
> The babe so small and helpless
> And watched by ass and dove,
> Who's visited by shepherds,
> Is Christ the Lord of love,
> And came from heaven above.
>
> The baby held so gently
> And rocked as Mary sings,
> Who's given precious golden gifts,
> Is Christ the King of kings;
> For him all heaven rings.

Little Star *picks up 'baby' and comes centre stage. She looks down at the 'baby'.*

Narrator   The Little Star was so thrilled to have learnt about Christmas at last. She looked forward to going back to the sky and telling everyone all about it.

Everyone stands, facing the audience to sing:
Finale song
Tune: Golden Slumbers (trad)

Down on the earth it's Christmas time.
Trees sparkle brightly, look so fine.
As Christmas day begins to dawn,
Remember that the Babe was born.

Birds in the winter sing each day
Hoping some crumbs will come their way.
As Christmas day ...

People rush by and never stop,
Buying their presents from each shop.
As Christmas day ...

Think of the stable far away,
Shepherds and wise men shown the way.
As Christmas day ...

Costume notes
Trees
Green or brown trousers and tops. Triangular tree shape in green fixed to front.
(Tree shape could be covered in fringed green paper or hands as in 'The
Christmas Tree' See instruction on p20)

Birds
Headband with beak and eyes. Plain tops and trousers or tights in suitable
colours eg black for blackbird, grey for pigeon, brown trousers and red top for
robin. Possibly 'wings' dangling from sleeves.

Shoppers
Outdoor clothes, small bag or basket.

Teacher and children
Nativity characters as appropriate. Readers and any ordinary children in 'smart'
clothes or school uniform. Teacher extra smart!!

Stars and Planets (see headdress suggestions below)
Milky Way – white robes, tinsel.
Orion's Belt – fastened together.
Moon – plain top and trousers (eg track suit in grey, navy, purple) with large
silver crescent moon on front.
Sun – similar, but bright colour (red, orange, yellow) with gold circle on front.
Planets – Togas or robes in white, yellow, orange or similar colours. (Mars in red)
Saturn has hoops round him (fixed to hang from shoulders)
Pole Star – carries star on stick.

Headdress suggestions for stars and planets
• tinsel
• band with stars
• band with one large star

- band with spikes bent down (long spikes, bend outwards before putting round head)
- possibly crown for Jupiter, Venus and Sun.

Narrator
Long plain robe or 'smart' clothes. Large book cover or folder entitled 'The Little Star' or plain dark blue with smaller silver stars on the background.

Gifts

by
Marjory Francis

This is more of a presentation than a play. It uses the subject of 'gifts' to tell the Christmas story, and then goes on to consider the gifts that we are able to present to God and others. It is left, therefore, for groups to include their own suggestions at various points. These are indicated in the text. Some children could play more than one part and in some places 'groups' could be just one person. Traditional and well-known carols and songs are used, but these are only suggestions and can be replaced by the users' own choices. If you wish the audience to join in with the carols, they could be announced. However, to maintain the flow of the presentation they could be sung by the cast alone or introduced simply by the music.

Background and props can be kept very simple. The background could be a plain curtain or dark blue with stars. Alternatively, it could be interspersed with flat boxes (eg cereal packets) covered with Christmas wrapping paper and fixed at different angles. You will need a manger and a bench or stool for Mary to sit on. You will also need a simple armchair or upright chair for Mrs Harris. These can be brought on to the stage as they are required.

Costumes can be simple too. The nativity group can wear traditional outfits, and the modern day groups as appropriate. You might like to consider colour groups, eg the readers all in blue or Group 1 in shades of browns and reds.

If this is used as a church presentation the six readers could stand up within the congregation to read their pieces. If they do so, make sure they can be heard. The five groups could emerge from different areas of the building.

Characters

Five speakers		
Announcer	Group 1	Mum
Six readers		Sally
Mary		Mrs Harris
Joseph	Group 2	'writers'
Innkeeper	Group 3	'entertainers'
Three shepherds	Group 4	'craftworkers'
Three angels	Group 5	Jack
Three wise men		Bob
Reader for prayer		Andrew

The presentation begins with the five speakers holding decorated boxes of a similar size. As they speak they turn over the boxes to reveal one letter at a time of the word GIFTS.

Speaker 1   We are glad you are able to join us for our Christmas celebration this year.

Speaker 2   We will be thinking about gifts.

Speaker 3   Firstly, God's gift to us.

Speaker 4   Secondly, gifts for the baby Jesus.

Speaker 5   And thirdly, the gifts that we can bring.

Carol: **In the bleak midwinter** *(last verse solo)*

Announcer   From the beginning of time God had promised that he would send a special person, a King, to save his people. All through the Old Testament men and women looked forward to his coming and wrote down the messages that God gave them about him.

Reader 1   A voice cries out, 'Prepare in the wilderness a road for the Lord. Clear the way in the desert for our God.'

Reader 2   Then the glory of the Lord will be revealed and all mankind will see it.

Reader 3   Jerusalem, go up on a high mountain and proclaim the good news. Tell the towns of Judah that their God is coming!

Reader 4   The people who walked in darkness have seen a great light. They lived in the land of shadows but now light is shining on them.

Reader 5   A child is born to us! A son is given to us! And he will be our ruler. He will be called 'Wonderful Counsellor', 'Mighty God', 'Eternal Father' 'Prince of Peace.'

Reader 6   The Sovereign Lord has filled me with his spirit. He has chosen me and sent me to bring good news to the poor, to heal the broken-hearted. He has sent me to proclaim that the time has come when the Lord will save his people.

Announcer   Jesus was the special person, the King, they were writing about. God sent Jesus at the first Christmas. Jesus – his special gift to us.

Carol: **See amid the winter's snow** (*selected verses*)

Mary *and* **Joseph** *enter.*

Mary   How much further is it to Bethlehem, Joseph? I am so tired.

Joseph   Not very far now, Mary.

Mary   I think the baby will arrive soon. Are you sure we have brought everything we need for him?

Joseph   Yes, I'm certain. I packed all the little clothes you made, and the blanket our friends gave us.

Mary   What a pity we couldn't bring the cradle you made so beautifully. Still, he will be able to sleep in it later on.

Joseph   Are you ready to go on now?

Mary   Yes, and I will try to hurry.

Joseph   What a blessing we have a willing little donkey to help us. Come along then.

Mary *and* **Joseph** *exit. They could walk round the outside of the audience/congregation during the song.*

Song: **Little donkey**

Enter **innkeeper** *towards the end of the song. He sets up the stool and manger to one side of the stage. Enter* **Mary** *and* **Joseph**.

Joseph   Are you sure you have nowhere for us to stay? We've tried everywhere else.

Innkeeper   I'm sorry. There are so many people in Bethlehem just now.

Joseph   But my wife is going to have a baby.

Mary   I think it will arrive very soon.

Innkeeper   Oh dear. But I really haven't any room to spare. There are even people using my own bed. Wait a minute though, there is the stable.

Joseph   The stable?

Innkeeper   Yes, I know it's not the best place, but at least you would be sheltered and your wife could lie down. I'll take you to it. (*Leads them to the stable area*) Here you are.

Joseph   Mary, I feel dreadful bringing you to a place like this.

Mary   Don't worry, Joseph. God knows all about it and he will look after us. Thank you for letting us use your last little space.

Innkeeper   That's all right. My animals can move up in the corner, and there is fresh hay in the manger so you could use it for a cradle. I'll bring you some hot soup later on.

Exit **innkeeper**. **Mary** *and* **Joseph** *remain, but 'freeze' until the* **shepherds** *and* **wise men** *arrive.*

Carol: **Away in a manger**

Enter **shepherds**, *rubbing their arms and blowing on their fingers. They bring in bundles and a sheepskin to sit on.*

Shepherd 1   It's cold tonight, Jacob.

Shepherd 2   You're telling me, Eli. Wish I had a nice woolly coat like a sheep on nights like this.

Shepherd 1   Everything quiet, Laban?

Shepherd 3   Yes, Eli. The sheep are all settled. I reckon we can have a bit of a rest now.

Angels *enter.* **Angel 1** *stands in between* **2** *and* **3** *a little in front of them. They all have arms outstretched with palms raised.*

Shepherd 2   What's that?

Angel 1   Don't be afraid. I come with good news from God.

Shepherd 3   Good news?

Shepherd 4   For us?

Angel 1   Yes, tonight God's promised one has been born. You will find him wrapped in strips of cloth and lying in a manger.

43

Angel 2   Glory to God!

Angel 3   Glory to God!

All angels   Glory to God in the highest heaven!

Exit **angels**.

Shepherd 2   God's promised one!

Shepherd 1   Born in Bethlehem! Let's go and see him!

Shepherd 3   Born in a stable! The poor little baby must be cold on a night like this. Let's take a warm sheepskin for him.

Shepherd 2   This is our best one. (*Picks up sheepskin.*) Let's take that.

Shepherd 1   Yes, and I've a good cheese my wife made. (*Picks up bundle.*) His parents will appreciate that.

Shepherd 2   Come on. Let's go!

While the carol is being sung, the **shepherds** *make their way to the manger. They can either move round the outside of the audience or exit and enter again. As the carol ends they lay their gifts at the manger, admire the baby, then join the tableau and 'freeze'.*

Carol: **While shepherds watched**

Wise men *enter*.

Wise man 1   I can't wait until it's dark to see if the star is there again.

Wise man 2   If we see it tonight we will know it is true that there is a wonderful new king.

Wise man 3   And if there is a new king we must go and pay him homage.

Wise man 1   We will start on our journey tomorrow. Are you both ready?

Wise man 2   My servants have been packing and loading my camels for the last week.

Wise man 3   I have chosen the best gift I can find for him – pure gold.

Wise man 1   I have a gift of frankincense.

Wise man 2   And I have myrrh. Only the most precious things are right for such a special king.

Wise man 3   Look, it is getting dark. Is the star there? *(Looking up)*

Wise man 1   *(pointing)* Yes, there it is!

Wise man 2   Then let us go to worship the king and give him our gifts.

The **Wise men** *move as the shepherds did during the carol, except that at some point they need to pick up their gifts. They lay these at the manger as they reach it.*

Carol: **We three kings**

Mary   My baby was born in a stable and laid in a manger, and yet we have been so blessed with food, clothing and precious gifts, but most of all with love and friendship.

Carol: **Hark the herald angels sing**

Solo: Repeat last verse of *In the bleak midwinter*: 'What can I give him?'

Each group comes in turn with a decorated box. They announce their gift and lay it at the manger before 'performing'.

Group 1   We give you the gift of our time.

Sally *sits down crosslegged at one side of the stage and reads a book.* **Mrs Harris** *goes to sit on a chair at the other side and gets out her knitting.* **Mum** *stays in the centre, looking towards Sally. They 'freeze' before the action begins.*

Mum   Sally, have you got a minute?

Sally   I'm busy, Mum. I'm reading.

Mum *(coming up to Sally)* Oh, there you are. Have you got a minute?

Sally   Oh Mum, I'm reading.

Mum   It's just that old Mrs Harris is poorly. She needs someone to pop to the shop for her. I thought you might like to do it.

Sally   Oh, I was just at the exciting bit. But poor Mrs Harris. I'll finish my book later.

Mum   Good girl. You pop off and see her.

Sally crosses the stage to **Mrs Harris**. **Mum** *'freezes' in the centre.*

Mrs Harris   Oh Sally. How kind of you to come. I just need a few things from the shop. Here's the list. (*She rummages in her knitting bag and produces a list.*)

Sally   Oh Mrs Harris, what lovely knitting. What are you making?

Mrs Harris   A sweater for my grandson. Would you like one? You be thinking what colour you'd like and I'll knit you one.

Sally   We can both use our time to help others.

The group 'freezes' before they exit.

Group 2   We give you the gift of writing.

This group read out some of their own writing, eg stories, poems or letters.

Group 3   We give you the gift of entertainment and making people happy.

This group perform in some way, such as dancing, gymnastics, juggling etc.

Group 4   We give you the gift of our skilful hands.

This group show work done with their hands, such as paintings, banners, models etc.

Group 5   We give you the gift of friendship.

The three boys 'freeze' before the scene starts. Jack and Bob stand together at one side of the stage, as if they are talking together, or playing something such as conkers. Andrew stands looking forlorn at the other side.

Jack   Who's that, Bob?

Bob   Oh, he's a new boy in our class.

Jack   What's his name?

Bob   Andrew I think.

Jack   He looks a bit lonely.

Bob   Well, I expect he doesn't know anyone.

Jack   I'm going to say hello. Hello, are you Andrew?

Andrew   Yes. Hello.

Jack   I'm Jack. I'm in the other class. Have you moved from far away?

Andrew   Not far, but I've left all my friends behind.

Jack   Yes, it must be lonely for you. Come and play with us, eh Bob?

Bob   Sure. Next playtime I'll bring my football out. Do you play football, Andrew?

Andrew   Yes, I was in the team at my last school and we won the cup.

Jack   In the team, eh? Won the cup!

Bob   We've picked a good friend here, Jack.

Jack   Haven't we!

The group 'freeze' before they exit.

Song: **The wise may bring their learning**

Reader   Let us pray. Thank you God for the gift of your Son, Jesus Christ. Help us to remember that as we give good gifts to others, we are giving to you. Bless us and our families this Christmas time as we celebrate this joyful time of giving. In Jesus' name. Amen.

The Story of the Little Angel

by
Angela Weir

Characters in order of appearance

The Angels, including:
Gabriel
Michael
Raphael
Simeon
Jonathan
Nathanael

Mary

Joanna, her friend
Isaiah, the Prophet
The Little Angel

The Shepherds, including:
John
Seth
James
Josiah
Matthew
Benjamin, the young shepherd

Joseph

The scene is in Heaven just before Christmas. There is a large gathering of excited **Angels**.

Simeon   Have you heard the news?

Nathanael   Yes. It's all very exciting, isn't it?

Jonathan   A special mission, so I believe.

Nathanael   I know. I can't wait to hear more. Do you know any more, Simeon?

Simeon   I haven't exactly got what it is we're supposed to be doing, have you, Raphael?

Raphael   Well, I've sort of got the idea, but I expect Gabriel will tell us properly.

Michael   I hope he does. I should hate to get a message as important as this wrong. It all sounds so strange.

Enter **Gabriel**

Gabriel   Ah, good. You're all here, I see. Now, do you understand your orders?

Michael   We think so, Gabriel, but we're not quite sure.

Raphael   No. Could you tell us exactly, please? Where is it we are to go?

Michael   He said we are to go to a field.

Raphael   That's what I thought he said, but I wasn't quite sure.

Simeon   Which field?

Raphael   That's what I want to know.

Jonathan   And what planet is it on?

Simeon   What planet?

Jonathan   Yes, what planet? There are quite a few you know.

Nathanael   It must be one of the big ones – he would hardly go to a small one.

Simeon   Of course he wouldn't. You're right, Nathanael.

Jonathan   But which one is it? There are several to choose from and we don't want to lose our way, do we?

Gabriel   Just be quiet a minute, all of you. Out there is a world full of people. They are selfish, thoughtless, and some of them are quite wicked, but God loves them. He made them, you see, and that makes them very special to him.

Jonathan   Where are they all?

Nathanael   Are they all over the universe?

Gabriel   No, no. They are just confined to one little planet. It's called Earth. Come over here. Look. You see down there? *(He points)*

Jonathan   Oh, yes. I can see. Look, Simeon, can you see it?

Simeon   Yes, it's beautiful. It's quite large, isn't it?

Gabriel   Wait a moment, you're looking at the wrong planet. Earth is more to the right, look.

Nathanael   What, that shiny little speck down there?

Gabriel   Yes, that's the one.

Jonathan   But it's so small.

Raphael   It's hard to believe that he is bothered about anything as small as that.

Simeon   Why ever did he choose that for all his people?

Gabriel   It's actually very beautiful. Not as wonderful as Heaven, of course, but it's still beautiful. But this is beside the point. He did choose it for his people and as you will remember, nine months ago I was sent on a mission.

Michael   It was secret at the time, wasn't it, Gabriel? Can you tell us about it now?

Gabriel   Yes, I can. But I think it would be more exciting if I showed you what happened. (*The* **Angels** *agree, and* **Gabriel** *indicates that they should clear a space. As they do so,* *Mary enters. She is followed by her friend,* **Joanna***)* This is Mary. She is very young as you see. She is kind, gentle and pure. She loves God, her Father, and worships him with all her heart.

Jonathan   Who's that with her, Gabriel?

Gabriel   Oh, that's her friend, Joanna. She's not particularly important to our story, but listen to what they say. It will tell you something about Mary.

Mary   Everything is going to be just fine, Joanna.

Joanna   Are you sure, Mary?

Mary   Of course. I have been praying that my parents would choose the right husband for me, and they have chosen Joseph. He must be the answer to my prayers.

Joanna   But how can you be so certain?

Mary   Because I trust God, my Father, to know exactly what is right for me.

Joanna   Joseph's an old man, Mary.

Mary   (*laughing*) Not that old. Anyway, he's kind and loving and gentle. I know he'll look after me. But nothing you say can spoil today.

Joanna   Why today particularly?

Mary   I don't really know, but ever since I woke up I had the feeling that today was going to be really special, quite different from any day I've ever known before.

Joanna   (*laughing*) I don't understand you at all, Mary, even though you're my best friend. I wish I had your faith and trust. I'd better go now. I promised Mother I would go to the market for her. Goodbye, Mary.

Mary   God bless you, Joanna. (*Joanna leaves and Gabriel steps forward to Mary*).

Gabriel   Peace to you, Mary. (*Mary is terrified and falls to the ground*).

Mary   Who are you, sir?

Gabriel   Do not be afraid. I am Gabriel, the Father's messenger, and I bring you very special news.

Mary   News? To me? What news?

Gabriel   Our Father has chosen you to be the mother of his Son, the Christ, who is to be born to save all men and bring them back to him.

Mary   Me, sir?

Gabriel   Yes, Mary.

Mary   How shall this be, sir? I am engaged to be married to Joseph, the carpenter.

Gabriel   Yes, Mary. The Father knows that. He also knows that there will be a lot of misunderstanding about the birth of his Son. But he has chosen you to fulfil the prophecy written many centuries ago by the prophet Isaiah, that a Saviour would be born to a pure virgin.

Mary   But what about Joseph, sir? He won't understand. He is a good man and I don't want to hurt him.

Gabriel   Of course you don't, Mary. The Father has thought about that. Will you trust him?

Mary   Yes, I must. It is hard sometimes, but I always try to trust him.

Gabriel   Good. The Father will speak to Joseph and tell him what is to be. And the Holy Spirit will come to you. Keep these things to yourself for the time being, Mary. God will bless you and help you. (*He goes back to the other* **Angels**.)

Mary   Oh, Father, I knew that today would somehow be different but I could never have believed how special it would be. I shall have to trust you more than ever now.

(**Mary** *exits. Enter* **Isaiah**. *He is flustered*).

Isaiah   But Gabriel, this isn't right.

Gabriel   What's the matter, Isaiah?

Isaiah   I prophesied all those years ago that the Christ would be born in Bethlehem, King David's city, not Nazareth. This girl lives in Nazareth. Didn't I hear the Father correctly?

Gabriel   Perfectly all right, Isaiah. God has it all planned. He has put it into Caesar's mind to call a census, and for this, everyone is going to have to go back to the city their family comes from, so that they can be taxed. Mary and Joseph are on their way to Bethlehem now.

Isaiah   But how does that make it right? Mary isn't a direct descendant of King David, is she? They have to be descendants of King David to go to Bethlehem, you know.

Gabriel   Joseph is a descendant, Mary's husband. That's why they are going to Bethlehem.

Isaiah   Ah, I understand. People all thought I was mad, you know, all this talk about a young girl giving birth to a Saviour.

Michael   Never mind, Isaiah, all the prophets have suffered in the same way. But the Father will fulfil every one of your prophecies, don't you worry.

Isaiah   It was hard at the time, you know, but I had to go on. The Father's voice was so insistent. I'm glad to know that I heard him right. *(He goes.)*

Jonathan   Nice old chap. Where do we come in, Gabriel?

Gabriel   It is our job to go and proclaim the good news to all mankind.

Jonathan   So where do we start?

Nathanael   It's obvious, Jonathan, we shall be going to the great king's palace first.

Gabriel   Wrong, Nathanael. We are going to a field.

Simeon   Oh, yes, you mentioned that before, but there won't be many people in a field, will there?

Gabriel   No, not very many, but enough.

Nathanael   I don't understand at all.

Gabriel   We can none of us understand the Father's ways, but we all have to trust, just as Mary has done, that he is right and he knows what is best for his people.

Raphael   Who are these people in the field? Has the Father gathered all the important people there specially?

Gabriel   No, Raphael, you know that is not his way. He always uses the poor and the humble to do his work. These are shepherds in the field.

Simeon   Shepherds? The outcasts from society! Everybody thinks the shepherds are stupid. They tell jokes about them. You know – "have you heard the one about the shepherd who..."

Gabriel   (smiling) Another time, Simeon! The Father loves them the same as he loves the great kings, and it is our job to go and tell the good news of the Saviour's birth to them. Now then, are you ready? (Just at this moment, the **Little Angel** enters.)

Little A   What's all the excitement? Is it true that you are all going on a special mission.

Nathanael   That's right, Little Angel. We're just off. Please would you stand aside.

Little A   Oh, can't I come, too? I've always longed to go on a mission.

Simeon   Not this time, Little Angel.

Little A   Oh, please let me. My wings won't grow if I can't come on a mission.

Nathanael   We know that. But you have to do at least one small mission on your own before you can come on an important one. You certainly haven't got enough experience to come with us this time. We're going to visit some shepherds.

Little A   Shepherds? But they aren't important.

Nathanael   These ones are, and they are all waiting for us in a field. We must go.

Little A   It's always the same. You're not experienced enough, you're not big enough. But I'll never grow unless you let me have some experience. That's how we grow, isn't it, Gabriel?

Gabriel   Well, yes, Little Angel, but not this time. Next time, I promise you. *(To the others)* Now, are we all ready? *(They answer him excitedly)* Best voices, remember. Come along all of you and don't lag behind. This way.

*(They exit, leaving the **Little Angel** behind)*

Little A   *(dejectedly)* It's always the same. They always leave me behind. They say "not this time," "you're too little for this one", but how will I ever grow unless I get the chance? I wonder if I dare follow? It's a long way I know, but my wings are getting stronger – I'm sure I can do it. A quick prayer first: Father, please come with me and protect me, otherwise I might get lost. Keep me strong, Lord, and please help my wings to get bigger. Amen. Here goes!

*(The **Little Angel** flies off after the others. The scene changes to the field. The **shepherds** are gathered there, cold and hungry).*

John   It's a cold night tonight.

Seth   Never seen the stars so bright, have you?

James   No – beautiful, isn't it?

Josiah   Now where's young Benjamin got to? He should have been here ages ago.

Matthew   Be patient, Josiah, the lad's only little. It's a long way for him to come up here all the way from the village.

Seth   I wouldn't like to make that journey this time of night. You never know what might happen.

Josiah   Oh, Benjamin's not afraid. And he's sure-footed, he'll find his way, don't you worry.

John   I'm glad he's not my son, I'd be worried about him.

Josiah   He'll be all right, I tell you. He's getting a big lad now.

Seth   How old is he now, Josiah?

Josiah   Well, I get confused a bit. I think he's – well, round about nine or ten, perhaps.

Matthew   Oh, that's really grown up, that is! I'm surprised your wife'll let him come.

Josiah   Look, do you want some food tonight or don't you?

Others   Of course we do, (*etc.,*)

Josiah   Well then – .

Seth   But you could have gone down to the village yourself, Josiah.

Josiah   What, me go down there? I don't like the dark, – not on my own, anyway. (*The others laugh*)

Matthew   Just as well Benjamin doesn't mind, eh?

Josiah   Stop getting at me. The lad's all right, I tell you.

John   What's going on in the village? I can see lots of lights from up here. That's not usual.

James   Haven't you heard? Everyone's had to gather for the census. It's jam-packed.

Seth   Oh, yes. My uncle and his family have had to come back from Galilee. They've been up there for years now. It was quite a trek for them.

John   Have you registered then?

Seth   Oh, yes. Well, the missus did it for me, me being up here 'n' all. My uncle and his family are staying with us at the moment – there was nowhere else. Everywhere's crowded. He was quite worried about a young girl who was travelling with them – her and her husband. The poor young thing is expecting any time now and they couldn't find anywhere to stay – nowhere, it was all full.

James   What happened then? Did your wife take them in?

Seth   Couldn't. Not possibly. Not with the rest of the family. No, she found them a place, though. Not ideal, mind you, but better than it might be I s'pose. The inn-keeper found them a place out at the back – in the stable.

Matthew   In the stable! Shouldn't like my kid born in a stable.

John   Nor me. Not much of a start in life.

James   Dark and dirty – and cold, I'll bet.

Seth   The inn-keeper did his best for them – put down new straw, you know. They seemed quite comfortable.

Josiah   You saw them, then?

Seth   Yes, I went to see if I could do anything. Took a rug for her to lie on. The baby should be born by now. It was nearly her time.

Matthew   Well, may the good Lord bless her then, and the baby.

Seth   Amen to that, Matthew. *(It is beginning to get brighter.)*

John   Hey, look what's happening up there!

James   What is it, John?

John   I'm not sure. It looks as if all the stars are crowding together.

Josiah   Can't be that. It's too bright.

Seth   And you can still see the stars anyway. *(They pause for a moment, looking up. It is getting brighter.)* Whatever's happening – it's getting brighter all the time.

Matthew   It looks as though the whole of heaven is opening up. It's terrifying.

Seth   Good Lord protect us! *(The **Shepherds** are terrified and throw themselves down on their faces. The **Angels** appear.)*

Gabriel   Do not be afraid. You have nothing to fear.

57

Matthew	Who are you, sir?
Gabriel	I am Gabriel, God's messenger angel, sent by him to give you special news.
Josiah	What news is that, sir?
Gabriel	News of the birth of the Messiah – the Anointed One.
Shepherds	*(to each other)* The Messiah – the Promised One – is he born?
Matthew	Where should we find him, sir?
Gabriel	Down there – in that little town.
Seth	In Bethlehem, you mean?
Gabriel	Yes. That's right. Just as the prophet foretold.
John	But is he truly born there, in Bethlehem?
Gabriel	You know the scriptures – the prophecy from Isaiah – that he would be born here. Well, it has come true this night.
James	But where should we go to find him, sir?
John	Yes, we must know where to find him.
Gabriel	You will find him in a stable.
Seth	A stable?!
Gabriel	That's right.
Seth	*(astonished)* But I – uh – in a stable! I think I know them.
Gabriel	Then you can show your friends the way, can't you!
Seth	Yes. No, I don't know – It couldn't have been them.
Gabriel	I think it could, Seth. That couple you saw. They are the ones.

*(The **Angels** exit, leaving the **Shepherds** excited and a bit bewildered).*

John   Goodness me. That was amazing. Was I dreaming?

James   Did you think you saw an angel?

John   Not just one. It seemed as though there were thousands.

Seth   That's what I saw too. It can't have been a dream.

Josiah   They said to go to the town – to see the new-born King. Didn't they?

Matthew   That's right. Well, what do you think? Shall we?

John   What, and leave the sheep?

Matthew   Yes. They'll be all right.

James   Do you suppose those angels are going round telling everybody?

Seth   I don't know. It'll be crowded at the stable if they are.

Matthew   Well, I don't know about you lot, but I'm off. I can't wait to see him. *(At this moment Benjamin enters carrying a heavy basket.)* Oh, hello, Benjamin.

Josiah   You've taken your time. Where have you been?

Benjamin   I'm sorry. This basket is heavy and it is very dark. I couldn't see where I was going – at least –

Josiah   At least – what?

Benjamin   Well, I was coming up the hill, in the dark, and all of a sudden it got brighter and brighter. It was as clear as day but just before I got here it all went dark again, except for that star.

Seth   Which star?

59

Benjamin   Look, that one. *(He points)* It's huge and so bright. I've never seen one like that before. It seems to be right above the town. Surely you must have seen it?

Seth   Yes, I've seen it. Come on, everyone, we must go to the stable. *(He begins to leave, the others following)*.

Benjamin   What made it all so bright?

James   Angels, thousands of them.

Benjamin   Angels! Did you see them?

Matthew   Yes, we did. We can't explain now. We've got to go.

Benjamin   But don't you want your supper?

Matthew   We haven't time. We must hurry.

Benjamin   Where are you all going – and what about the sheep?

Josiah   Stay there till we come back. You'll be all right.

*(All the **Shepherds** leave)*.

Benjamin   It's always the same. The messenger boy, the food carrier and the sheep-minder when there are more important things to do. *(He looks round and then draws close to the fire.)* I can't see the angels any more. What a pity, I'd love to see one. The sheep seem to be quite happy. It's very cold. I wonder how long they will be? I want to get back to bed. *(At this moment the **Little Angel** arrives, very out of breath.)*

Little A   Phew! What a long way, but I've made it. And all on my own. Thank you, Father. Now then, where have they all got to? I'm sure this is the place they came to – I could see them as I was coming down. *(He sees **Benjamin**)*. Oh, hello. Who are you?

Benjamin   My name's Benjamin. Who are you?

Little A   *(impressively)* I'm an angel. *(No reaction from Benjamin.)* Well, aren't you impressed?

Benjamin   Not really. I thought angels were huge.

60

Little A   (*sadly*) I'm still only a little angel. I keep hoping I'll grow, but the others always leave me behind when they go on missions. Usually when people see angels they get very frightened because they're so big – but you're not frightened of me – (*hopefully*) are you?

Benjamin   No. Sorry. I thought I saw all the other angels. It was certainly very bright.

Little A   That would be them. They came to tell the shepherds that the new King has been born. Can you believe it – God has actually been born as a baby here on earth! Amazing, isn't it?

Benjamin   It's hard to understand. How could he make himself into a tiny baby?

Little A   I don't know. I don't understand either, but I just know he has. And he's been born in Bethlehem – tonight!

Benjamin   Really? Is that where the other shepherds have gone?

Little A   I expect so.

Benjamin   Do you think we could go too? (**Gabriel** *enters.*)

Gabriel   Ah, there you are, Little Angel. I wondered what had happened to you.

Little A   Gabriel! I didn't think you knew I was following you.

Gabriel   Of course I knew. The Father told me. You know we can't keep any secrets from him.

Little A   I thought he might have other things on his mind tonight. (*Gabriel laughs and then turns to Benjamin who is scared stiff.*)

Gabriel   He never has too much on his mind. Now, Benjamin, don't be afraid. Tonight is very exciting.

Benjamin   Are you really Gabriel?

Gabriel   Yes.

Little A   (to **Benjamin**) You're impressed by him, aren't you?

Benjamin   Of course. He's huge.

Gabriel   Do you want to see the new King?

Benjamin   Oh, yes, please, sir.

Gabriel   Then come along. (The **Little Angel** hesitates) You too.

Little A   Can I really? I'm not in disgrace?

Gabriel   After flying all that long way by yourself, certainly not. And you brought the message to our young friend here.

Little A   Thank you, Gabriel. May I lead the way?

Gabriel   Do you know which way to go?

Little A   Yes. Down to the big inn with the stable at the back. Isn't that right?

Gabriel   (smiling) Yes, go on. We'll follow, won't we, Benjamin?

Benjamin   Can I take him a present – one of the lambs?

Gabriel   That's a kind thought, Benjamin, but just give him yourself – that's all he wants.

Benjamin   Myself? How do I do that?

Gabriel   By trusting him and doing what he asks you to do.

Little A   Can we go now?

Gabriel   Yes, Little Angel, lead on. We're close behind you, aren't we, Benjamin?

Benjamin   Of course. I'm not missing out on this.

(They exit and the scene changes to the stable. **Mary** and **Joseph** are there with the **Shepherds**).

Seth   May we come in, lady?

Mary   Yes, welcome, friend. Have you come to see the baby?

Josiah   That's right. We – er – heard about it when we were up on the hills.

Joseph   Do come in, all of you. How did you hear?

James   It was a bit unusual really, wasn't it, John?

John   Yes, it was, rather. We – er – saw angels, you see.

Mary   Angels. They came to tell you about the birth of this baby?

James   Yes, that's right. It sounds a bit odd, doesn't it?

Seth   They said he is the Messiah.

Joseph   Yes. We have been told this too. Come and see him.

John   Is it really true?

Joseph   We believe it.

(The **Shepherds** *gather round the crib to see the Baby, then Gabriel enters with the* **Little Angel***, whose wings have grown, and* **Benjamin***.)*

James   Look who's here, Josiah.

Josiah   What are you doing here, Benjamin? We told you to mind the sheep.

Benjamin   I had to come.

Josiah   *(a little annoyed)* But you were supposed to be looking after the sheep.

Matthew   That doesn't matter now, Josiah. The sheep will be all right. This is what is important.

James   Who's that with you, Benjamin?

Benjamin   This is the Little Angel. He showed me the way.

63

(He looks at the **Little Angel***)* Hey! Look! We can't call you the Little Angel any longer – your wings have grown! It must have been that long journey.

Little A   It was worth coming all that long way just to see this. But I'm glad my wings have grown – now I'll be able to go on missions with the others.

Joseph   We welcome you. For his sake, we welcome you. Come close, both of you, come and see him. (**The Little Angel** *and* **Benjamin** *go together and kneel beside Mary to see the baby.)*

Mary   This night God has come to earth to show his love to everyone. May his peace and blessing rest upon you at this Christmas time.